Bear in the Park

Written by Miriam Simon

Illustrated by Julie Park

D1448165

Sam and Rosie were in the park.

They were playing hide and seek.
Rosie hid behind a tree.

3

Sam looked for her.
He looked behind a tree but
he didn't see Rosie. He saw . . .

a bear !

Sam ran to his mum.
He shouted, 'Mum! Mum!
There's a bear in the park.'

8

'No Sam,' said his mum,
'There are no bears in the park.'

Sam hid behind a bush.

Rosie looked for him.

She looked for him behind a bush.

But she didn't see Sam.

She saw . . .

a **bear** and a
kangaroo too!

Rosie ran to her mum.
She shouted, 'Mum! Mum! There's a
bear in the park and a kangaroo too!'

'No Rosie,' said her mum.

'There are no bears in the park and there are no kangaroos.'

'Yes there are,' shouted Rosie.

'I saw them.'

'And I saw the bear,' said Sam.

'It was behind a tree.'

Sam and Rosie went to look.
They saw the bear and the kangaroo.

'How do you do?' said the kangaroo.

'Come to the fair,' said the bear.

Sam ran to his mum.

He shouted, 'Mum! Mum!

There's a fair in the park! Can we go?'